50 Reasons I Fell In Love With You: A Fill In The Blank Book From Me To You

Other Books by the author:

Reignite Your Relationship by 7X
365 Days of Love for Us: An A-Z Coloring Book for Couples

Website: www.marshaunolaniyan.com

Follow Marshaun on your favorite social media sites:

YouTube: MarshaunO

Instagram: marshaun

FB Fanpage: Marshaun Olaniyan

Dedication

This book is dedicated to every couple who is being intentional about keeping their fire burning for one another.

1.

I fell in love with you

when you

_____

_____.

2.

My favorite memory of

us together is

_____

_____

_____.

3.

I love it when you tell the

story about

_____

_____.

4.

I cannot help but laugh

every time you

_____

_____.

5.

I love it when you

_____

_____

_____.

6.

I cannot stop thinking

about the time you

_____

_____.

7.

Your kiss makes me

feel _____

and reminds me of _____

_____.

8.

**I love your aroma. It smells
like** _____
_____.

9.

Our first date was

_____

_____

_____.

10.

I fall in love every time you

_____

_____

_____.

11.

You light up when you

_____

_____

_____.

12.

My favorite thing to do with you is

_____

_____.

13.

I'm always pleasantly

surprised that you

remember

_____

_____.

14.

I'm inspired by your

_____

_____

_____.

15.

You make me feel

beautiful when you

_____

_____

_____.

16.

You are thoughtful

when you _____

_____

_____.

17.

Your generosity makes

me _____

_____.

18.

Your smile

_____

_____

_____.

19.

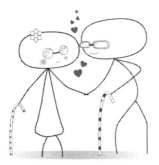

I can't wait to grow old with you so we can _____

_____

_____.

20.

My heart skips a beat

when you _____

_____

_____.

21.

Your hugs _____

_____

_____.

22.

It turns me on

whenever you_____

_____

_____.

23.

It always brings me

pleasure when you

_____

_____ .

24.

You can be weird when

you _____

_____**, but**

I love you all the same.

25.

If I had to sum up what

you mean to me in one

word, it would be

_____.

26.

When we are apart I

feel _____

_____

_____.

27.

Every time I hear

_____

song, it makes me

think of you.

28.

My favorite holiday

with you is

_____

_____.

29.

We have the best time

whenever we _____

_____

_____ **together.**

30.

Watching you _____

_____ **gives me so much**

joy. It makes my heart

_____

_____**.**

31.

Loving you is like

_____

_____

_____.

32.

I love that you make

me _____

_____

_____.

33.

You make me feel super

_____

_____ **whenever I'm down**
and need a pick-me-up!

34.

Choosing you was

_____

_____

_____.

35.

If you were a cartoon

character you would be

_____

because

_____

_____.

36.

I'd love for us to _____

_____

_____.

37.

I love seeing you wear

the color _____.

It brings out your

_____

_____.

38.

I love looking into your

_____

_____.

39.

I feel safe whenever

you _____

_____ **for me.**

40.

My world is brighter

every time you _____

_____

_____.

41.

If you were a car you

would be a _____

because _____

_____**.**

42.

I love watching you

_____

_____.

43.

You are the kind of

_____

every _____

_____ **wishes for.**

44.

I love how

passionate you are

about _____

_____.

45.

Because of you, the

tough times seem less

_____

_____.

46.

You make the best

_____

_____

_____.

47.

The first thing I noticed

about you when we

first met was your

_____

_____.

48.

I love how you make

me _____

whenever I'm _____

_____.

49.

Your best feature, in my

opinion, is _____

_____.

50.

The top three words

that sum up how much

I love you are _____,

_____ **and**

_____.

Manufactured by Amazon.ca
Bolton, ON